GARFIELD
WORDS OF WISDOM

JIM DAVIS

RAVETTE BOOKS

First published by Ravette Books Limited 1992

Printed and bound for
Ravette Books Limited
3 Glenside Estate, Star Road, Partridge Green,
Horsham, West Sussex RH13 8RA
An Egmont Company
by Proost International Bookproduction, Belgium

ISBN: 1 85304 401 6

GARFIELD
Party animal

JON'S PARTY APPEARS TO BE GOING WELL

I'LL HIDE IN HERE TILL DESSERT IS SERVED

1989 United Feature Syndicate, Inc.

HOW ABOUT SOME FONDUE, EVERYBODY?

YAAAAAA

GARFIELD! YOU'RE SITTING IN THE PUNCH BOWL

OH SURE! TRY TO CHANGE THE SUBJECT, YOU CANNIBAL!

JM DAVIS 2-12

Toast Of The Town

Get Your Skates On!

BREAKFAST, GARFIELD!

SQUEAKA
SQUEAKA
SQUEAKA

SQUEAKA
SQUEAKA

SQUEAKA!
SQUEAKA!
SQUEAKA!

CRASH!

© 1989 United Feature Syndicate, Inc.

DO BE SO KIND AS TO LEVEL THE TABLE, WOULD YOU PLEASE?

JIM DAVIS 3-5

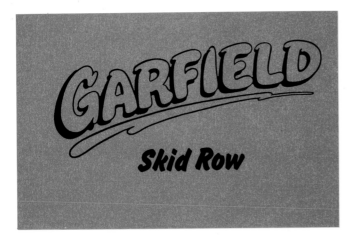

Pas de Deux

Tiptoe through the tulips

Nappy days are here again

© 1989 United Feature Syndicate, Inc.

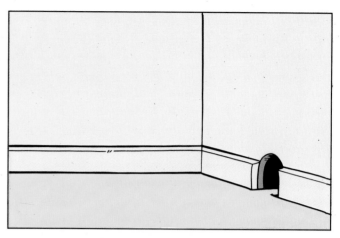

© 1989 United Feature Syndicate, Inc.

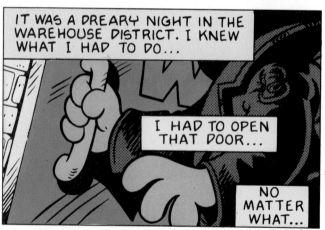

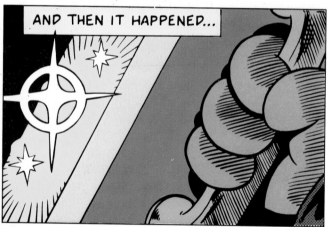

Surfin' USA

The Birthday Boy

Cracking up

JIM DAVIS

6-18

OKAY, I'LL BE THE BIRTHDAY CAT, AND YOU BE THE CAKE:

♪ HAPPY BIRTHDAY TO ME, HAPPY BIRTHDAY TO MEEE, HAPPY BIRTHDAY DEAR GARFIELD, HAPPY BIRTHDAY TOOO MEEE!

FOOF!

DO YOU KNOW WHAT LAZY IS?

LAZY IS TAKING A COFFEE BREAK BETWEEN NAPS

THERE ARE TWO RULES FOR ASSEMBLING A MODEL AIRPLANE...

NEVER GET GLUE ON YOUR HANDS. AND, IF YOU DO...

NEVER PICK YOUR NOSE

I HAVE TO GO TO THE HOSPITAL NOW

They say you can judge a man by his tie. Mine's like me — stripey and large!

OTHER TITLES AVAILABLE IN THIS SERIES

GARFIELD

No. 1 Sitting Pretty

HAGAR

No. 1 The Hero

LUCKY LUKE

No. 1 The Dalton Brothers
        Memory Game

MARMADUKE

No. 1 Canine Capers

PINK PANTHER

No. 1 Through The Hoop

SNOOPY

No. 1 Swings Into Action

THUNDERBIRDS

No. 1 To The Rescue
No. 2 In Space

TOM & JERRY

No. 1 Copy Cat
No. 2 Sweet Temptation

£3.99 each

Additional titles will be added to this series, for a complete list please contact Ravette Books.

All these books are available at your local bookshop or newsagent, or can be ordered direct from the publisher. Just tick the titles you require and fill in the form below. Prices and availability subject to change without notice.

Ravette Books Limited, 3 Glenside Estate, Star Road, Partridge Green, Horsham, West Sussex RH13 8RA

Please send a cheque or postal order and allow the following for postage and packing. UK – 50p for one book and 35p for each additional book ordered.

Name ....

Address ....

....